ORIGINAL PIANOFORTE PIECES

BOOK I
(Preliminary & Grade 1)

THE ASSOCIATED BOARD OF
THE ROYAL SCHOOLS OF MUSIC

A Little Story

FELIX SWINSTEAD

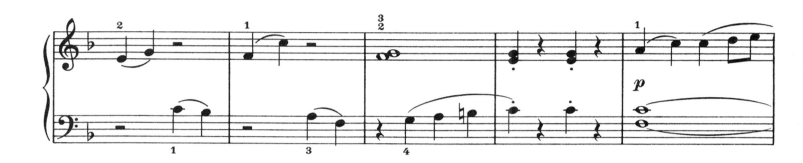

The Lonely Road

FELIX SWINSTEAD

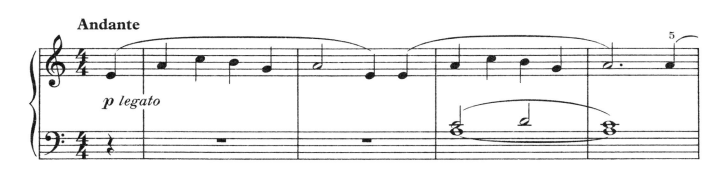

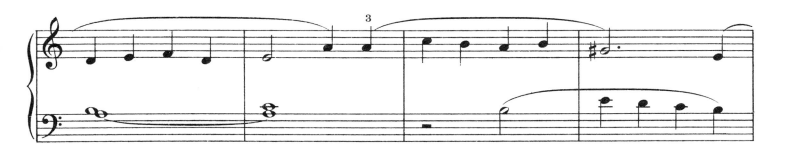

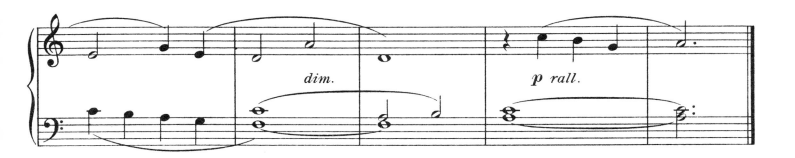

4

Rain

E. MARKHAM LEE

Moderately quick

Pit-ter, Pat-ter

f

f sempre staccato

The Bonnie Briar Bush

E. MARKHAM LEE

The Old Windmill

THOMAS F. DUNHILL

From *First Year Pieces*, published by the Associated Board

AB 1728

A Song of Erin

THOMAS F. DUNHILL

Andante con moto

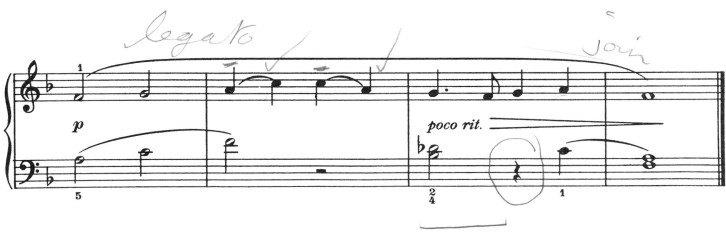

From *First Year Pieces*, published by the Associated Board

Robin Redbreast

JESSIE FURZE

Cheerful Sparrows

JESSIE FURZE

The Pear Tree is Laden with Fruit

WILLIAM ALWYN

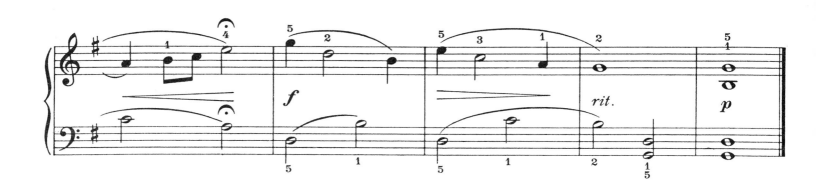

AB 1728

A Windfall of Apples

WILLIAM ALWYN

Dance of the Toads

LESLEY BAMFORD

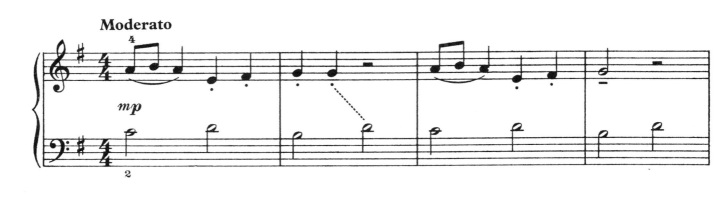

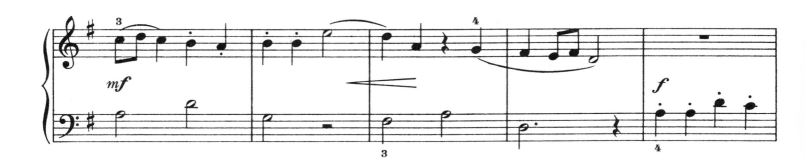

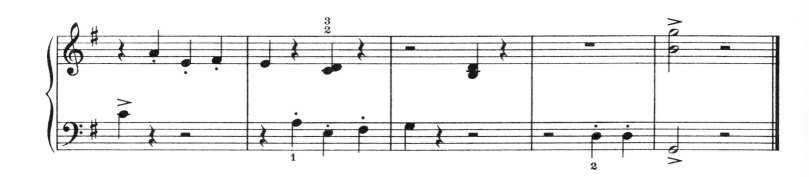

Night March

LESLEY BAMFORD

On the River

WILLIAM H. HARRIS

Upstairs and Downstairs

WILLIAM H. HARRIS

Fine

D.C. al Fine

Mill-wheel Slowly Turning

DOROTHY HOWELL

An Argument

DOROTHY HOWELL

Lullaby

GEORGE DYSON

From *12 Easy Piano Pieces*, published by the Associated Board

Air

GEORGE DYSON

From *12 Easy Piano Pieces*, published by the Associated Board

Gavotte

GUY WARRACK

Gracefully

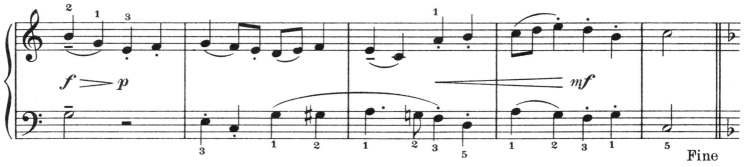

Fine

Gavotte D.C. al Fine

Winter-time

GUY WARRACK

A Swing Song

BASIL C. ALLCHIN

A Holiday Tune

BASIL C. ALLCHIN

A Tender Flower

FELIX SWINSTEAD

Gliding

FELIX SWINSTEAD

From *Work and Play*, published by the Associated Board

Prelude in F

JEAN CAVET

A Little Old Dance

HEDWIG McEWEN

The Drummer Boy

JESSIE FURZE

Falling Leaves

JESSIE FURZE

The Bassoon Player

LESLEY BAMFORD

Distant Bells

LESLEY BAMFORD

Moderato

The Quiet Wood

MICHAEL HEAD

Slow, with singing tone

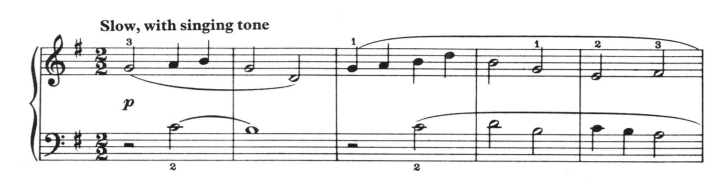